THE GRAPHIC STORY OF THE TRAFALGAR WAY

THE PICKLE AT
TRAFALGAR

*Being an account of how news of the great battle was carried to
Britain and set before the King by Lieutenant John Richards
Lapenotiere, Commanding Officer, HM Schooner Pickle.*

ILLUSTRATED BY
RON TINER

SCRIPT
JOHN FISHER

ADDITIONAL ARTWORK & ILLUSTRATION
GRAHAM KENNEDY

WITH AN INTRODUCTION BY
CAPTAIN PETER HORE, RN

PERETTI PUBLISHING, DEVON, ENGLAND

TO EVERYONE who helped this small book along the way,
our sincere thanks, especially to Max Adams, Harry Axbey,
Rodger Barton, Commander Peter Blanchford, RN,
Helen Breeze, Alfredo Comparini, Ron George,
Captain Peter Hore, RN, Richard James, James Lee,
Deirdre Livingstone, Roma E. Richards, Matthew Sheldon,
Rear Admiral Robin Shiffner, CB, RN, Barbara and
David Stewart-Wheeler, Bill White and Dr Colin White.
Also Joe Fisher, who first lifted me up to view the model of the
Battle of Trafalgar, then housed at the National Maritime Museum,
Greenwich (and nowadays at the Royal Naval Museum,
Portsmouth) thus providing me with my first glimpse of and the
idea for *The Pickle at Trafalgar.*

John Fisher, Devon

For Maggie

The Pickle at Trafalgar
Copyright © John Fisher
First published in 2005 by
PERETTI PUBLISHING
PO Box 18, Ottery St Mary, Devon EX11 1YU, UK
www.perettipublishing.co.uk

Before the Battle and *Home is the Sailor* are reproduced by kind
permission of the author, Captain Peter Hore, RN.

Illustrations Copyright © Ron Tiner
Book design Joe Pieczenko

British Library Cataloguing in Publication Data
A Catalogue record of this book is available from the British
Library
"The Pickle at Trafalgar"
Fisher, John

ISBN 0 906038 10 3

BEFORE THE BATTLE

BY CAPTAIN PETER HORE, RN

THIS IS A TRUE ACCOUNT of how a naval lieutenant, an eye witness to the battle of Trafalgar, raced to bring Admiral Collingwood's dispatches to Britain and later set out the story in a unique way at Windsor, across the King's breakfast table.

Lieutenant John Richards Lapenotiere, was commanding officer of HM Schooner *Pickle*, the second smallest British ship present at the battle. He was born at Ilfracombe, Devon in 1770. His family appears to have come to Britain at the time of his great-grandfather, Frederick De La Penotiere who was the son of a French nobleman, a Huguenot who had settled in Holland and probably came to Britain with William of Orange or one of his followers, in 1688.

He first went to sea aged 10 in the hired armed ship, *Three Sisters*, and by 1784 had served in two warships on the West Indies station. At 15 he signed on as a Gentleman Volunteer in a hired merchant ship, *King George* and a year later became part of a commercial expedition to trade American furs in China. Following this three year voyage of circumnavigation he returned to become a midshipman, first in the 14-gun brig *Scout*, and then the 74-gun ship *Magnificent*.

Lapenotiere returned to the Pacific in 1792, on board the *Assistant*, which accompanied Captain William Bligh's ship, *Providence* on his second breadfruit expedition. In 1793 he joined the 36-gun frigate *Santa Margarita* as Master's Mate, and may have seen action ashore when, a year later, Admiral Sir John Jervis's squadron landed *"a division of 300 seaman and marines to drag up guns and mortars to assist the army ashore"* in the siege of Fort Bourbon, in Martinique.

He was made lieutenant in April 1794, aged 24, and given command of the 8-gun brig *Berbice*.

He served as lieutenant in various ships in the North Sea and the Channel and then in 1800, obtained the command of the 8-gun hired cutter *Joseph*. He *"was several times engaged with the enemy, near Brest, and then employed in affording protection to the Mediterranean trade. On each of these occasions, his gallant conduct obtained him the high approbation of his commander-in-chief, Earl St. Vincent and Sir James Saumarez."*

On 24th May 1802, aged 32, Lapenotiere took command of another small vessel, the 10-gun schooner *Pickle*. Her original name had been *Sting*, *"a clever fast sailing schooner of about 125 tons, coppered and in every respect suited to the Service"* and she was purchased in the West Indies in December 1800 for £2,500. Built, almost certainly, at Bermuda in 1799, she was 73 ft (22.25m) overall, 56 ft 3 ins (17m) on the waterline, 20 ft 7 ins (6.25m) in breadth, and 9 ft 6 ins (2.9m) in depth and measured 127 tons (129 tonnes), and armed with six carronades, either 12 or 18-pounders.

The *Pickle* carried 42 men, the youngest, a volunteer, was aged 14 and the oldest, an Irish ordinary seaman (who deserted before Trafalgar) was aged 40. Most were in their early twenties. Typical of the British fleet off Trafalgar, just under half of her crew were English, and of these, about a quarter of the whole, were from Devon and Cornwall. At Trafalgar the crew included two Americans – John Oxford, and the Master, George Almy, both from Newport, Rhode Island.

Pickle was part of Admiral Cornwallis's blockading fleet off Brest, and when the line-of-battle ship 74-gun *Magnificent* sank after striking on the Black Rocks on 25th March 1804, the *Pickle* rescued some of her crew.

In July 1805 on passage from Plymouth to Gibraltar, *Pickle* got into a scrap. As she was becalmed in the Straits in the afternoon of 19th July, she was attacked by two, well-manned Spanish gunboats who kept up a heavy fire with grape and shot until the wind sprang up and the *Pickle* could reply with broadsides and in her turn began to chase the Spaniards towards Tarifa.

When the wind fell again the Spaniards were reinforced by seven other gunboats, and the tables turned again. Lapenotiere tacked towards Tangier, but the Spaniards under oars were quicker and got within gun range again, keeping up a continuous fire from *Pickle's* stern arc where she could bring no gun to bear. Anchoring under the Fort of Tangier, one of the gunboats anchored near the *Pickle* and the others remained loitering outside the bay. The *Pickle's* rigging was damaged and one man slightly hurt by splinters, but that was all the damage, and when a regular breeze sprang up again *Pickle* was easily able to evade the watchers and rejoin the fleet.

Admiral Sir Cuthbert Collingwood, reading Lapenotiere's despatch thought he had acted with *"great spirit and propriety opposed as he was to a sort of force... [Spanish Gun boats, which swarm here] ...which with his short Guns, he could give no annoyance at the distance they kept."* It seems that the *Pickle* was only a fast sailer in heavy weather, because Collingwood in his despatch referred, in the light airs prevailing, to her indifferent sailing and inability to come up with the enemy.

Back in Plymouth on 3rd September 1805, Lapenotiere asked for a Sub Lieutenant *"as there is no Person onboard... capable of rendering any Service in Case of an Accident happening to me."* The Admiralty appointed John Kingdon, who arrived onboard on 20th September and the *Pickle* sailed almost at once with another draft of seamen for various ships of Nelson's fleet off Cadiz.

Here then was the ship, the crew, the man and the hour. Which is where our story begins...

Overleaf: John Richards Lapenotiere, aged 35, from a water colour in the possession of the family.

Below: Jack Tar gives 'Old Boney' a drubbing. Detail from Gillray cartoon © National Maritime Museum, London

SHATTERED VICTORY

First light, Sunday 27th October 1805: six days after the Battle of Trafalgar

The combined French and Spanish fleets have been defeated

Britain is now safe from invasion, but Vice-Admiral Lord Nelson is dead and the shattered VICTORY is in tow to Gibraltar

After the storms of the Bay of Biscay, the winds fall away

Off the Scillies, they are becalmed and are forced to take to the sweeps for five gruelling hours

Some of PICKLE's crew are from Devon and Cornwall where there was once a widely-held belief that the "joyful and dreadful news" was shouted to a fishing boat out of Penzance

...and that, some hours later, word reaches the Mayor of Penzance during a ball at The Union Hotel

The PICKLE finally makes landfall on Monday 4th November at Falmouth

A contemporary print of Falmouth Harbour

The PICKLE is known along this coast as a dispatch vessel, and quickly attracts a crowd hungry for news

PICKLE

But Lapenotiere confines himself to the exchange of pleasantries

His news is for the Admiralty, in London and he rents a post chaise

It has not rained in England since 30th October...

...but it will not be an easy journey

The 271-mile dash from Falmouth to London...

is made in a little over 36 hours, stopping 21 times...

...to change horses, postillions and post chaises

Expenses for the journey, later reimbursed by an Admiralty clerk, will be £46.19s.1d – nearly half a Lieutenant's annual salary in 1805

As Lapenotiere nears Honiton in Devon, Captain Sykes arrives at Plymouth, where there is no news of The PICKLE

He is ordered to make post haste to the Admiralty

The distances between them open and close as day turns into night, and night becomes day again

Lord Barham is woken to be given the news

Clerks are roused from their sleep and the news is copied

The King, at Windsor, and Prime Minister Pitt must be the first to be told

But Lapenotiere's mission is not yet over

The Battle of Trafalgar ▶

THE BATTLE OF TRAFALGAR

NAPOLEON'S long-held plan to invade England was finally torn from his grasp when the British fleet intercepted and destroyed the combined French and Spanish fleets off Cadiz, at Cape Trafalgar on 21st October, 1805.

Vice-Admiral Horatio Lord Nelson's flagship is HMS VICTORY

Caught heading for the Mediterranean, the enemy fleet turns to flee northwards again – but it is too late

Nelson's attack plan has the British fleet form into two columns to cut the enemy line

Repeatedly hit by enemy broadsides during her long approach, VICTORY holds her fire

Shortly before Victory comes under fire, Nelson makes his famous signal ENGLAND EXPECTS THAT EVERY MAN WILL DO HIS DUTY

Fallen masts and trailing rigging lock ships into death struggles as they exchange broadsides at point blank range

Whilst Nelson's life ebbs away below deck, the fury of the battle increases and much of the fighting becomes hand-to-hand

Then she cripples the French flagship, BUCENTAURE with a broadside fired through her stern windows

At the battle's height a sharpshooter in the French REDOUBTABLE targets Nelson and he falls, mortally wounded

The battle won, Nelson's great friend Captain Hardy reports "we have taken 14 or 15" enemy ships without the loss of a single British vessel

Nelson's last words, whispered to Hardy are, "Thank God, I have done my duty"

THE TRAFALGAR RECKONING

IN MEMORY of the men and boys – as well as the uncounted numbers of women – of the British and combined French and Spanish fleets, who were killed or subsequently died of their wounds or were drowned in the great storm following the Battle of Trafalgar, 21st October, 1805.

BRITISH BATTLESHIPS AT TRAFALGAR

NELSON'S WEATHER COLUMN

BRITISH (12)	Guns	Killed	Wounded
Victory	104	57	75
Temeraire	98	47	76
Neptune	98	10	34
Leviathan	74	4	22
Conqueror	74	3	9
Britannia	100	10	40
Spartiate	74	3	53
Minotaur	74	3	20
Ajax	74	2	2
Agamemnon	64	2	7
Orion	74	1	21
Africa	64	18	37

COLLINGWOOD'S LEE COLUMN

BRITISH (15)	Guns	Killed	Wounded
Royal Sovereign	100	47	94
Belleisle	74	33	93
Mars	74	29	69
Tonnant	80	26	50
Bellerophon	74	27	123
Colossus	74	40	160
Achille	74	13	59
Defence	74	7	29
Defiance	74	17	53
Agamemnon	64	2	7
Dreadnought	98	7	26
Revenge	74	28	51
Swiftsure	74	9	8
Thunderer	98	4	12
Polyphemus	64	2	4

FRIGATES

Euryalus, Naiad, Phoebe, Sirius,
Juno (not present at the battle), *Pickle* (schooner),
Entreprenante (cutter)

COMBINED FLEET BATTLESHIPS AT TRAFALGAR

(in order of sailing)	Guns	Killed	Wounded
Neptuno (S)	80	38	38
Scipion (F)	74	17	22
Intrepide (F)	74	("Half the crew")	
Formidable (F)	80	22	45
Duguay-Trouin (F)	74	12	24
Mont-Blanc (F)	74	20	20
Rayo (S)	100	4	14
San Fransisco de Asis (S)	74	5	12
Heros (F)	74	12	26
San Agustin (S)	74	184	201
Santisima Trinidad (S)	130	216	116
Bucentaure (F)	80	197	85
Redoubtable (F)	74	490	81
San Justo (S)	74	0	7
Neptune (F)	80	15	39
San Leandro (S)	64	8	22
Santa Ana (S)	112	104	137
Indomptable (F)	80	("Two thirds")	
Fougeux (F)	74	(546)	
Pluton (F)	74	60	132
Monarca (S)	74	101	154
Algesiras (F)	74	77	142
Bahama (S)	74	75	66
Aigle (F)	74	("Two thirds")	
Montanes (S)	74	20	29
Swiftsure (F)	74	68	123
Argonaute (F)	74	55	137
Argonauta (S)	80	103	202
San Ildefonso (S)	74	36	129
Achille (F)	74	(480)	
Principe de Asturias (S)	112	54	109
Berwick (F)	74	("Nearly all drowned")	
San Juan Nepomuceno (S)	74	103	151

FRIGATES

Cornelie (F), *Hermione* (F), *Hortense* (F), *Rhin* (F),
Themis, Argus (brig), *Furet* (brig)

HOME IS THE SAILOR

LAPENOTIERE was promoted Commander, and the Patriotic Fund gave him a sword worth 100 guineas, which stayed in the family for over a hundred years. So too did the silver muffineer - now part of the civic treasure of Liskeard – which had been given him by the King at the end of their meeting.

He also received a share of the prize money, though much smaller than the share received by the captains of the line-of-battle ships. The reward for the *Pickle's* crew was more despatch duties. However, under the command of Lieutenant Daniel Callaway she captured, in January 1807 a French privateer cutter, *la Favorite* of 14 guns and a crew of twice her size. *Pickle's* career came to an end on 27th July 1808 under the command of Lieutenant Moses Cannadey, when she grounded on the Chipona Shoal off Cape Santa Maria, on her approach to Cadiz. She quickly filled and sank, but all were saved.

In 1806, Lapenotiere, now a Commander, was appointed to the 16-gun brig *Orestes*, with complement of 95 officers, men and boys. The *Orestes* missed the Second Battle of Copenhagen in 1807, but formed part of a squadron which after the battle was stationed in the Sound to protect trade. There Lapenotiere suffered a dreadful accident.

While in the Elsinore Roads, he was frequently *"obliged to stand in so close with the enemy's batteries, for the purpose of ordering away the different vessels that have anchored there during the night... [and]... exposed to their fire... This happened again yesterday; and in firing one of the after guns, by some unforeseen accident, it communicated to a drawer, containing the powder-horns and a few cartridges, the explosion of which, I am sorry to say, has so far disabled me, as to prevent, I fear, my being able to perform my duty, for some time to come."*

His injuries seemed quite horrific, *"The skin of my face, ears, and neck, is completely burnt off; and the greater part of the hair off my head, the skin of which I fear must follow. But what concerns me most, is, that I am in some danger of losing my right eye likewise. The whole of the right side of my head is much contused, by a piece of plank forced against it by the explosion. I am at this moment obliged to keep my bed,"* though like the heroes of the age he seems to have recovered quickly.

After his recovery, Lapenotiere and the *Orestes* were employed in the Channel, where he captured a 12-gun privateer, *la Concepcion*, and retook an American ship bound to Plymouth with timber. On the 9th May 1810, with *la Favorite* (now under the White Ensign) he took the 10-gun French schooner *la Dorade* and on the 27th October Lapenotiere took the 16-gun French privateer *le Loup Garou*. According to Marshall *"she kept up a smart fire for about thirty minutes ... a remarkable fine vessel, well found in everything, and calculated to do much mischief to our trade."* Admiral Sir Robert Calder wrote that *"this capture does very great credit to the captain, officers, and men of the Orestes, from the prompt and neat manner in which it has been effected, without any loss to his Majesty's service; and confirms the good opinion I have long since entertained of Captain Lapenotiere as an officer, whilst serving under my command at different times."*

Lapenotiere obtained post rank on 1st August 1811 and retired to live quietly in Cornwall with his second wife, Mary Ann, daughter of the late Lieutenant John Graves, whom he had married in 1805. They had seven children, at least one of whom was in the navy by 1828. Most of his descendants appear to have emigrated to Canada and America. He died on 23rd January, 1834 at Roseland, Menheniot, aged 63.

The only permanent memorial which Captain John Richards Lapenotiere has left in Britain is a boundary marker in the wall of the garden of his house at Menheniot, near Liskeard, Cornwall, a short distance from the churchyard which is his final resting place. His sword and a portrait are in the National Maritime Museum at Greenwich. ∎

Portrait of Captain John Lapenotiere (above)
© National Maritime Museum, London

The Royal Navy has always remembered the *Pickle* and the part she played in bringing the news from Trafalgar. Since 1808 there have been a further eight ships of the name. This is HMS *Pickle*, 1942, an Algerine class minesweeper.
Photograph ©Royal Naval Museum, Portsmouth

We are indebted to Captain Peter Hore for his kind permission to borrow so freely from his essay on John Lapenotiere used in the production of our prologue, Before the battle and epilogue, Home is the sailor.
Peter Hore is the author of *The Habit of Victory – the story of the Royal Navy*, published by Sedgwick & Jackson.

The muffineer artwork within our graphic narrative and on our back cover is based on a photograph by John Rapson of Liskeard